How to
TIE A
HEADSCARF

---

30 simple, modern styles

ALICE TATE

POP PRESS

CONTENTS

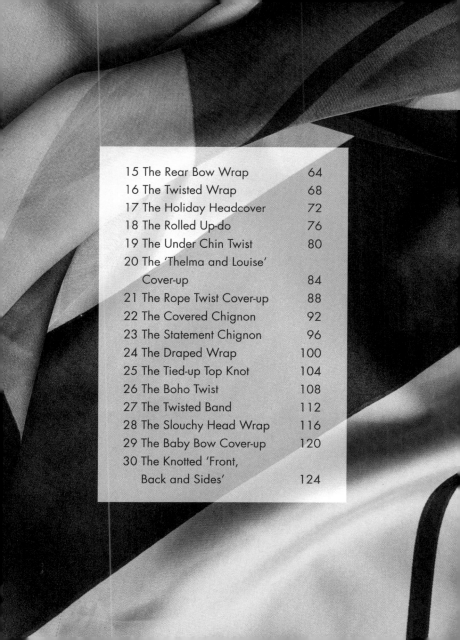

INTRODUCTION

From the functional to the chic, the headscarf is the ultimate accessory. Whatever print or style you choose, scarves can be worn in so many ways to create infinite different looks, from vintage inspired to contemporary, and are great for all hairstyles.

The 30 styles in this book have been carefully curated to make sure you are covered in the most beautiful ways whatever the occasion – holidays, office days, nights out, beach trips, festivals, bad hair days and everything in between.

BASIC FOLDS

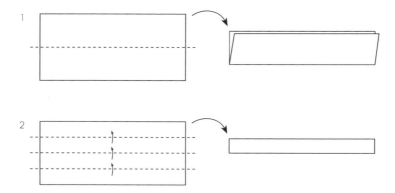

HEADSCARF BASICS

Fabric types that work well: Silk, viscose, chiffon, cotton and jersey.

Two basic headscarf shapes you need: 1 x square scarf – at least
50 x 50cm, though 90 x 90cm is the most versatile size.
(Other square scarves used here are 60 x 60cm and 70 x 70cm)

1 x rectangular scarf – at least 50 x 170cm.
*(Other rectangular scarves used here are 60 x 170cm, 70 x 170cm,
70 x 180cm, 70 x 190cm and 90 x 180cm. A long, thin rectangular
scarf is also useful – we've used one here that is 20 x 190cm.*

3

Elastics/
Hair bands

Hairspray

Hair doughnut
(for maximum volume
on top knot)

Hair grips

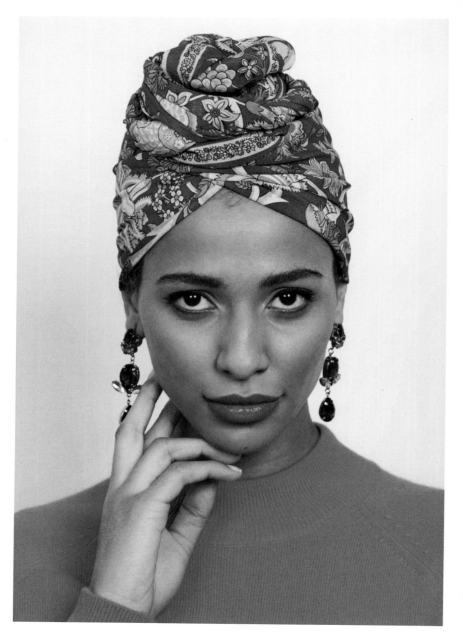

1

The KNOTTED WRAP

1 : The
KNOTTED WRAP

An easy-to-master style that works great with braids. Pair with sunnies, earrings and a bold lip to add a touch of glamour.

We used a 70 x 190cm scarf to create this look.

Tie your hair into a tight top knot.

Fold a long, rectangular scarf in half length ways.

Position the folded edge of the scarf at the base of your head, just above the nape of your neck (1).

Tightly pull the rest of the fabric over your head to the centre of your forehead (2).

Separate the two ends of the scarf and twist together until they resemble a rope (3).

As you do so, start wrapping this rope into a bun at the top of your head. When you reach the end, tuck the loose ends under the bun to secure (4). Pin in place to keep it secure.

For the finishing touch, add earrings to bring the whole look together.

1

2

3

4

2

The TUCK-AWAY WRAP

2: The
TUCK-AWAY
WRAP

A wrapped up, sophisticated style that works for everyone, and is best done with a large, rectangular scarf. Add a statement lip, specs, or earrings for a polished finish.

We used a 90 x 180cm scarf to create this look.

Using a long scarf, position one of the long edges at the front of your head, along the hairline.

Take the ends over your ears and cross over at the back of your neck (1).

Wrap one end of the fabric (folded flat) around your head, secure in place (2), then wrap the other side around your head, starting slightly further back to add a little height (3).

Tuck the end of the fabric underneath to secure in place (4).

1

2

3

4

3

The HEADBAND

3: The
HEADBAND

A versatile style that transforms a simple up-do into a more finished look. Works best with a long, thin strip scarf. Looks great with statement earrings.

We used a 90cm square scarf to create this look.

Tie hair up into a high ponytail or bun.

Using a thin, long scarf or a scarf folded into a neat long strip, wrap the fabric tightly around the head (1), securing at the nape of the neck with a knot (2).

Tuck the ends of the fabric underneath to neaten and secure in place (3).

1

2

3

4

The RIBBON BRAID

4: The
RIBBON
BRAID

Transform a simple braid into a sartorial statement by weaving in a printed headscarf. Easy-peasy wow factor.

We used a 70cm square scarf to create this look.

Tie the hair into a low ponytail and tie the scarf around the elastic to cover the band (1).

Separate the hair into three strands as you would a plait, adding the two ends of the scarf into the outer sections (2).

Plait the hair loosely, incorporating the fabric as you go (3).

When you get to the end, either tie with an elastic (4), or, if there is enough of the fabric left, you can wrap the ends of the scarf around the plait to secure and fasten into a bow.

Pull out strands and wispy bits to give a more relaxed and effortless look.

1

2

3

4

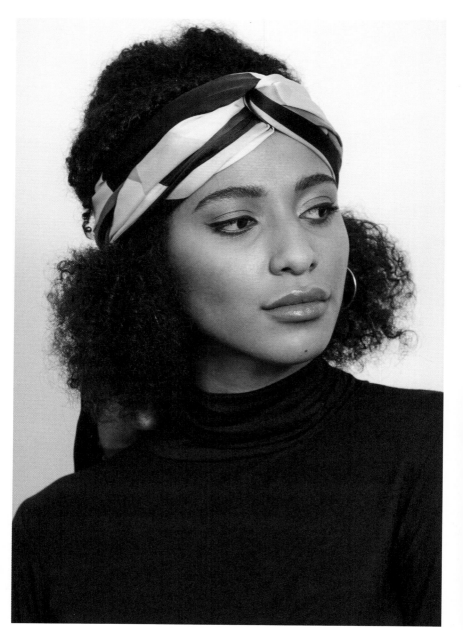

5

The PARISIAN TWIST

5: The
PARISIAN TWIST

Add a touch of Parisian chic to your ensemble with this relaxed, twisted band style that works best with a low, loose ponytail.

We used a 70 x 180cm scarf to create this look.

Fold a rectangular scarf to create a long band or use a long, thin scarf for this look.

With the hair down or in a low, relaxed ponytail, take the scarf to the nape of the neck.

Bring both ends up, over the ears, until they cross at the top of the head (1).

Then twist at the forehead until they are, once again, in line with the band (2 & 3).

Bring the ends back down, past the ears, to knot securely at the back (4 & 5).

Pull out any loose, wispy strands to give a more relaxed finish.

1

2

3

4

5

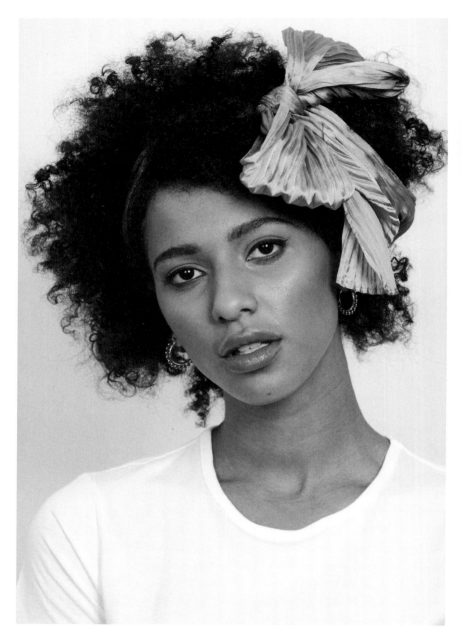

6

The BOHO BOW

6: The
BOHO
BOW

Transform a basic up-do into a cool, hippie look with this relaxed boho bow – an easy outfit finisher. Works well with a fringe and wispy bangs.

We used a 20 x 190cm scarf to create this look.

Tie the hair into a comfortable ponytail or low bun if you have long hair, or leave down.

Pull out the front strands or fringe to give a more relaxed look.

Take a long, thin scarf to the back of the neck (1).

Tie both ends into a comfortable bow at the front (2).

Pull the ends to make the bow as large or as small as you wish, and position slightly to the side (3).

1

2

3

7

The FORTIES WRAP

7: The
FORTIES
WRAP

Channel times gone by with this retro forties wrap – an easy-to-master style that makes the perfect accessory for a vintage look.

We used a 70cm square scarf to create this look.

With hair tied up at the back of the head, fold a square scarf into a triangle and place the fold at the nape of the neck. The triangle should be resting on the forehead (1).

Draw the two ends of the fabric up over your ears to meet at the top, and tie tightly (2), trapping the point underneath so the fabric covers the back and crown of the head.

Tie the ends of the fabric, including the point, into a bow, and pull out any loose strands to create a more relaxed look.

1

2

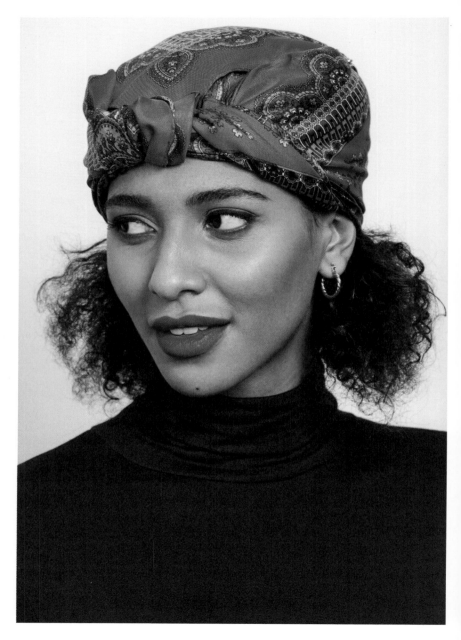

8

The MESSY HAIR HIDEAWAY

8: The
MESSY HAIR HIDEAWAY

Cover a million sins – bad hair days, dirty roots and flyaways – with this statement headscarf that works well with your hair up or down.

We used a 90cm square scarf to create this look.

With hair left loose, fold a large, square scarf into a triangle and take the fold to the base of the head (1).

Pull both layers of the point over the head and both ends up, past the ears, to meet at the top.

Tie all ends into a knot so the scarf sits securely on the head (2).

Once in place, tuck the ends of the scarf under the front so they're hidden, and let the last layer you tuck under cover the knot (3 & 4).

1

2

3

4

9

The PIRATE SCARF

9: The
PIRATE
SCARF

A simple, bohemian-chic style that adds a touch of glamour to any outfit. Works best with the hair left loose – a great trick for hiding unwashed roots.

We used a 90cm square scarf to create this look.

With the hair left loose, take a large, square scarf and fold it into a triangle.

Pull the scarf over your head so that the long point of the scarf is either to the left or right of your head (1 & 2).

Tie the ends together, trapping the fabric and the point underneath (3).

Arrange as feels and looks comfortable, then tie the ends into a bow (4).

1

2

3

4

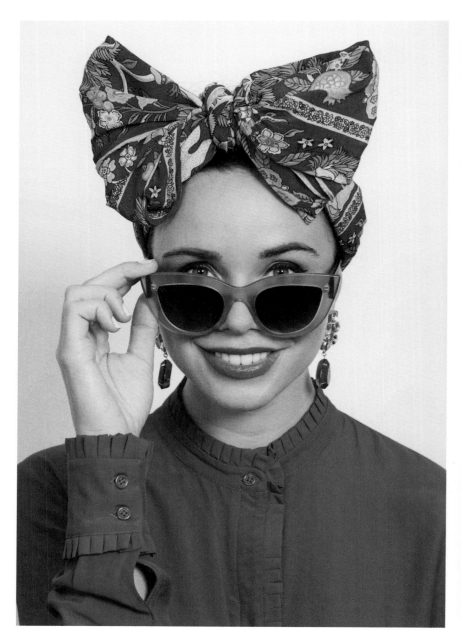

10

The STATEMENT BOW

10: The
STATEMENT BOW

Go big and go bold with this statement style that will add real drama to your look. Pair with sunnies, a bold lip or earrings for a polished finish.

We used a 70 x 190cm scarf to create this look.

Ideally, use a stiff, structured fabric for this style.

Tie hair into a tight top knot.

Place the headscarf at the back of the head, with one of the long edges lowered to the nape of the neck.

Tightly pull the rest of the fabric round to the front, and tie in a knot at the centre.

Tie the fabric into a bow (1), hiding the ends within the folds so you're left with a statement, oversized bow (2).

1

2

11

The HIPPIE HEADBAND

11: The
HIPPIE
HEADBAND

Channel hippie cool with a
retro headband worn with
loose tousled waves – great
for festivals, beach trips
and holidays.

We used a 90cm square scarf
to create this look.

For this style, it's best to use a silk
scarf for its thinness.

Take a square headscarf
and fold it into a triangle,
then fold again to make a
thick band.

With the hair left loose in
a centre parting, wrap the
folded scarf around the
forehead (1).

Tie tightly, so it doesn't
slip, at the back with a
knot (2 & 3).

To amplify the hippie
vibe, you can work
plaits into the hair before
wrapping the headband.

1

2

3

12

The MAIDEN TWIST

12: The
MAIDEN
TWIST

This pretty, maiden-inspired style will add a unique finish to any outfit, and it looks just as good all year round. Works best with a chiffon or thin cotton scarf.

We used a 50 x 170cm scarf to create this look.

Position one edge of a long, rectangular scarf on your forehead, with the fabric draped over the head (1).

Take the ends of the scarf to the back and cross over, trapping the loose fabric underneath so the scarf is in place like a hat (2).

Tightly twist the ends of the fabric to create rope-like strands that you can wrap around the head (3), crossing at the front (4), then tuck them in to secure in place (5).

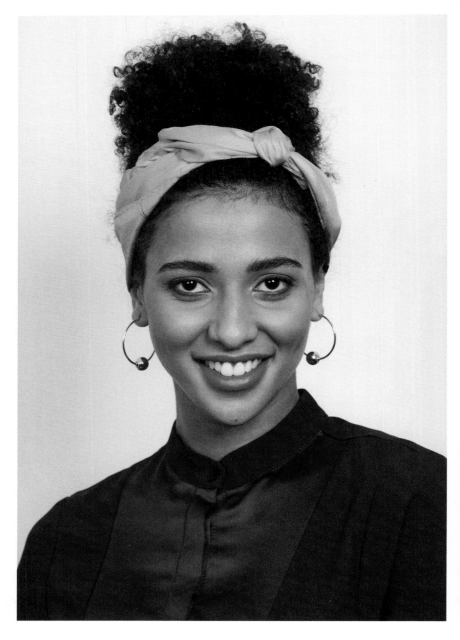

13

The KNOTTED BAND

13: The KNOTTED BAND

Add an elegant, ballerina-inspired finish to your up-do with this easy-to-master knotted headband style.

We used a 70cm square scarf to create this look.

Tie hair into a top knot.

Fold a square scarf into a triangle, then twist until it resembles a long, thin band.

Take to the back of the head and pull the ends of the scarf up to meet at the front (1).

Tie tightly at the top of the head so the band sits securely and comfortably over the ears (2).

Tie a second knot to secure in place (3) and then neaten it up (4).

Tuck the loose ends of the scarf under the band to create a chic and complex-looking wrap (5).

14

The ROLLERS COVER-UP

14: The
ROLLERS
COVER-UP

Keep your rollers covered and neat with the help of a headscarf – a timeless style that's both functional and fashionable.

We used a 70cm square scarf to create this look.

Take a large, square scarf and fold it into a triangle, then place the fold at the nape of the neck (1).

With the curlers in place, pull the ends of the fabric up over the ears to meet at the top, and tie tightly in a knot, trapping the point underneath so the fabric covers the whole head (2).

Finally, fold the loose triangular point back on itself to conceal the knot (3). Tuck the scarf ends underneath (4).

1

2

3

4

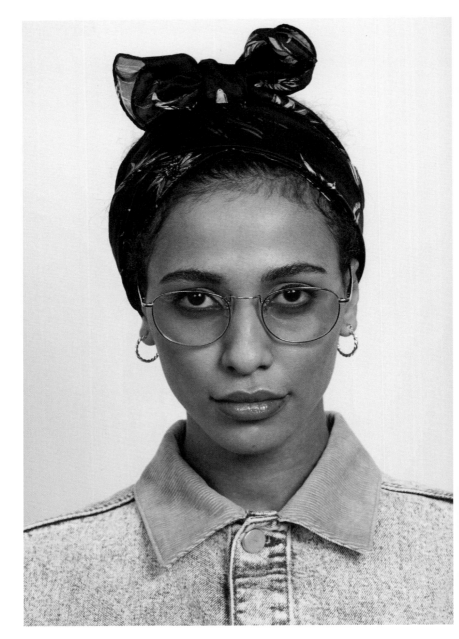

15

The REAR BOW WRAP

15: The
REAR BOW WRAP

Business at the front, party in the back. A ladylike twist on a traditional headwrap that's easy to master but adds instant sass to any look.

We used a 60 x 190cm scarf to create this look.

This look works with hair up in a ponytail or down.

Take a large, rectangular scarf (perhaps folded in half lengthways if a very thin fabric), and put it over the head with one of the long edges along the hairline and the other at the nape of the neck (1).

Draw the ends of the scarf up, to cover the ears and cross over at the top of the head (2).

Bring the ends down to cross again at the base of the head (3), then back up to meet at the top, where you'll just have two short ends of the scarf left.

Cross over and tie the ends of the scarf at the crown of the head into a knot or small bow and use a safety pin to secure in place.

1

2

3

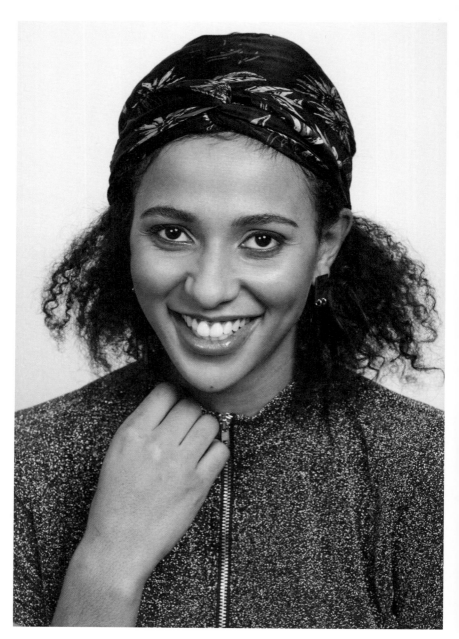

16

The TWISTED WRAP

16: The
TWISTED
WRAP

A stylish, statement finish to any outfit that works just as well with the hair up or down. Switch up your scarves with different patterns for different looks.

We used a 60 x 190cm scarf to create this look.

With hair down or in a loose, low bun or ponytail, position the scarf over your head with the long edge on your forehead, just below the hairline (1).

Cross the ends of the fabric at the nape of your neck and pull tightly round to the front to meet at the centre of the forehead (2).

Twist the ends over each other once or twice, tucking the ends of the fabric underneath the scarf to secure in place (3). If your scarf is very long, knot it at the back first and then tuck the ends under.

1

2

3

17

The HOLIDAY HEADCOVER

17: The
HOLIDAY HEADCOVER

Say bye-bye to beachy blowaways with this knotted headcover that looks elegant and relaxed, while keeping everything in place.

We used a 60cm square scarf to create this look.

With hair in a low bun, ponytail or chignon, fold a square scarf in half to create a triangle.

Take the fold to the top of the forehead (1), leaving your fringe loose if you have one, and draw the ends of the fabric to the back of the head.

Tie the ends in a knot or bow, trapping the point of the triangle underneath to create an elegant covered look (2 & 3).

1

2

3

18

The ROLLED UP-DO

18: The
ROLLED
UP-DO

A more complex style that works best with longer hair to create an elegant, bohemian look – one to practise, master and wear to impress.

We used a 70cm square scarf to create this look.

This style works best with day-old hair or textured hair. Dry shampoo is an easy way to add a bit of instant texture.

Tie hair into an ultra-loose ponytail, so that the elastic is towards the lower end of the ponytail.

Take a square scarf and fold it into a triangle then fold it again to make a band.

Position the scarf over the elastic (1) and roll it towards the base of the head, winding the hair around the scarf as you go (2 & 3).

Pull and position the hair as you roll, so it evenly covers the scarf and sits comfortably at the base of the neck (4).

Bring the two ends to meet at the top of the head (5), then tie in a knot to secure (6).

Loosely pull out some of the hair around the hairline to give a more effortless look. If you have really long hair, you might want to secure the hair roll with pins.

1

2

3

4

5

6

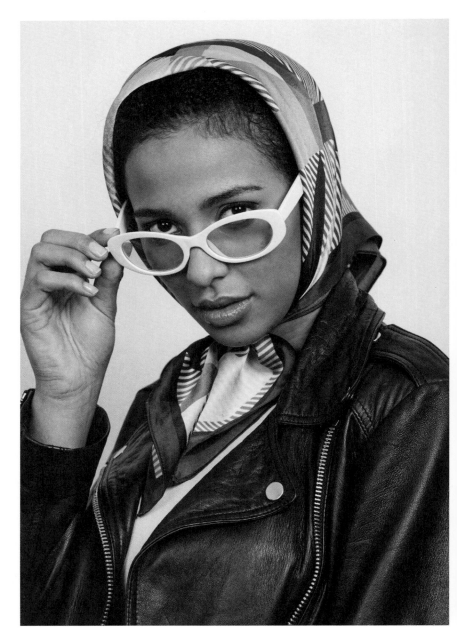

19

The UNDER CHIN TWIST

19: The
UNDER CHIN TWIST

A classic style favoured by both Queen Elizabeth II and Audrey Hepburn, this one is timeless, sophisticated and ladylike. Use different prints for different aesthetics.

We used a 70cm square scarf to create this look.

Fold a square silk scarf into a triangle and place the fold along the hairline with the point facing down towards the back of the head (1).

Tie the two ends into a single knot under the chin and tighten until the scarf feels comfortable and secure (2).

Once in place, fasten into a double knot (3). You might want to play with the fabric a bit to achieve a more natural look.

1

2

3

20

The 'THELMA AND LOUISE' COVER-UP

20: The
'THELMA AND LOUISE' COVER-UP

Take note from Thelma and Louise with this timeless, sleek and functional style that keeps everything in place – flyaways, fringes, chignons, the lot.

We used a 90cm square scarf to create this look.

It's important to use a large enough scarf for this style or you'll not have enough fabric.

Fold a large, square scarf into a triangle and place the fold over the head along the hairline with the point facing down your back.

Cross the two ends of the scarf under your chin (1) and wrap around the neck, trapping the point of the scarf (2) so the fabric is pulled tightly and securely over the head.

If the scarf is especially large, tuck in the point at the back after you've secured the knot (3).

Tie the ends in a small knot at the side of the neck to fix in place (4).

1

2

3

4

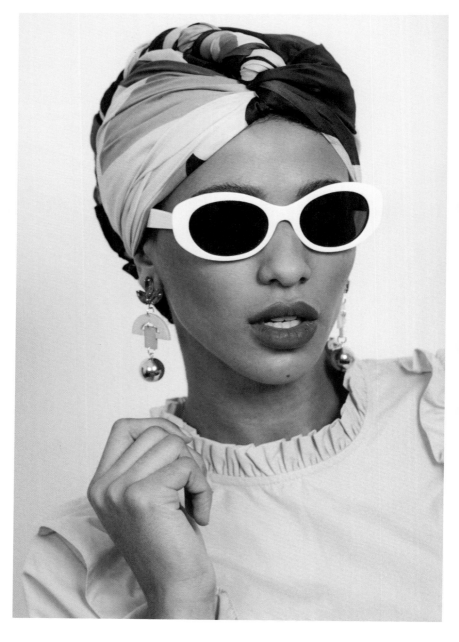

21

The ROPE TWIST
COVER-UP

21: The
ROPE TWIST COVER-UP

This looks great for getting your hair out of the way through the summer months. Get it up, twist, and tuck. So easy!

We used a 70 x 180cm scarf to create this look.

Tie hair into a high, tight ponytail.

Place a long, rectangular headscarf at the back of the head, with one of the long edges at the nape of your neck (1).

Tightly pull the rest of the scarf round to the front, then twist the fabric so that it sits tightly and securely around the head (2).

Once fully twisted, take this 'rope' towards the back of the head and tuck underneath the scarf at the nape of your neck to fasten in place (3–5).

Finish the look with a pair of statement earrings.

1

2

3

4

5

22

The COVERED CHIGNON

22: The COVERED CHIGNON

A sleek and striking style that's sure to put the finishing touch on any fashion-forward outfit. Best with a printed silk or cotton scarf – and sunnies are a must!

We used a 70cm square scarf to create this look.

This style works best with the hair tied into a loose chignon.

Fold a square, silk scarf into a triangle and place the fold over the head along the hairline with the point facing down your back (1).

Draw the two ends of the fabric to meet underneath the chignon and fasten in a small knot, tight enough for the scarf to stay securely on your head (2).

Tuck the points of the scarf left over the chignon underneath the knot (3).

Finish the look with statement earrings or a bold lip.

1

2

3

23

The STATEMENT CHIGNON

23: The
STATEMENT
CHIGNON

Turn a relaxed look into something bright, different and unexpected by weaving a printed scarf into a loose chignon – a great day-to-night outfit addition!

We used a 50cm square scarf to create this look.

Tie the hair into a loose, low ponytail.

Take a long, thin scarf and wrap a couple of times around the elastic, so that you end up with equal lengths of the scarf left loose.

Begin to braid the hair, weaving in the scarf ends as you go, and then fasten securely with an elastic band (1).

Loosely wrap the braid into a bun (2) and pin in place to secure (3).

1

2

3

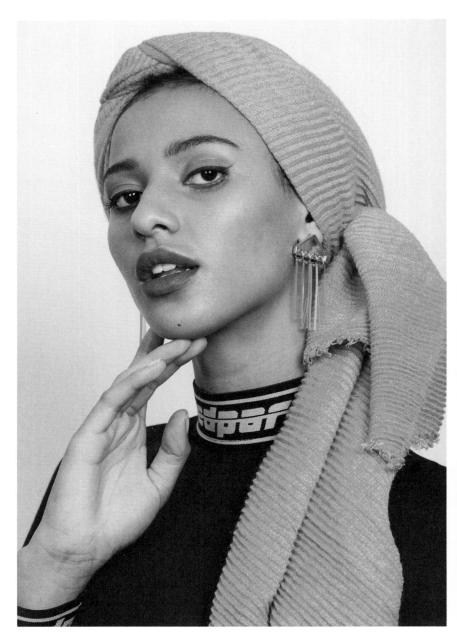

24

The DRAPED WRAP

24: The
DRAPED WRAP

Perfect for the winter months and sure to add impact to a laidback look. Use an oversized scarf for maximum effect!

We used a 70 x 100cm scarf to create this look.

The bigger the scarf the better this look works.

With the hair tied in a low bun, take the long edge of a large scarf to the hairline at the front. Bring the ends past the ears to tie, at the nape of your neck (1).

Draw both ends back round to the front and tie again at the top (2).

Take one of the ends directly down, past the ear, and the other, more loosely, over the back of the head and then around to meet at the ear (3). Tie both ends in place here with a secure knot (4).

Leave the remainder of the scarf to drape from this knot over the shoulder, to create a slouchy but statement style.

1

2

3

4

25

The TIED-UP TOP KNOT

25: The
TIED-UP
TOP KNOT

Win the top knot game with the help of a silky square scarf. A foolproof way to make a simple hairstyle impossibly chic.

We used a 50cm square scarf to create this look.

Tie the hair into a top knot. A hair doughnut is a good way of adding extra volume, and you may need pins to keep everything in place (these can be covered by the scarf).

Once secure, take a small, square silk scarf and fold it into a triangle, then fold again to create a band.

Take this to the base of the top knot at the front (1) and tie tightly with a double knot at the back (2). Leave the scarf ends to hang loose.

1

2

26

The HIPPIE TWIST

26: The
BOHO TWIST

Turn your loose holiday locks into something more styled with a printed headband. It keeps your hair in place and looks great with loose waves, plaits or full braids.

We used a 60 x 190cm scarf to create this look.

With the hair left loose, in braids or plaits (a centre parting works best for this style), take a long, thin scarf to the back of the head (1) and bring both ends round to cross the forehead.

With a single twist at the front (2), turn each end back on itself to meet at the back.

Before you fasten, take one end under and the other end over the first layer of the band to keep it all together (3), then tie a small double knot (4).

1

2

3

4

27

The TWISTED BAND

27: The
TWISTED
BAND

A feminine finish to any outfit
that works well with long
hair, incorporating both a
headband and a braid.

We used a 70 x 180cm scarf to
create this look.

Start by tying your hair
into a loose, low side
ponytail.Tie a knot in
the centre of a long,
rectangular scarf (1).

Take the scarf to the top
of the head, positioning
the knot to one side, and
tie under the ponytail so
the band feels secure and
comfortable (2).

Take the ponytail out so
the hair is loose and begin
to twist (or braid) the scarf
into the hair (3).

When you reach the end,
fasten the hair and scarf
with an elastic (4).

You might want to play
with the twist a bit to
loosen it and give it a
more relaxed look. You
also may want to add pins
to the hair around the ears
to keep the scarf in place.

1

2

3

4

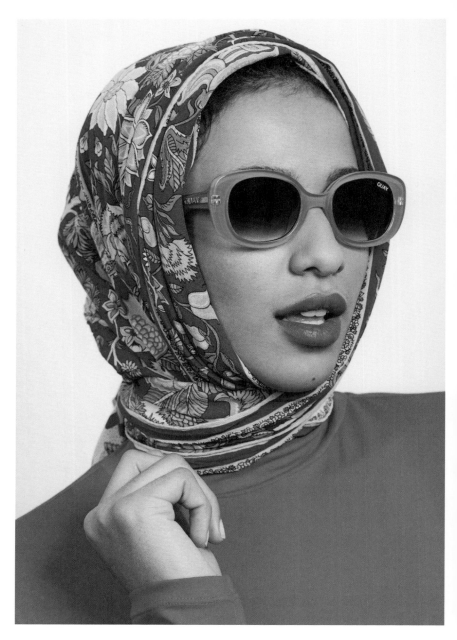

28

The SLOUCHY HEAD WRAP

28: The
SLOUCHY HEAD WRAP

A relaxed, slouchy take on a traditional hijab that's easy to create and easy to wear – great for weekends and lazy, low-key days.

We used a 70 x 190cm scarf to create this look.

Take a long, rectangular scarf over the head and fasten with a safety pin under the chin (1).

Twist one of the ends of the scarf until it resembles a rope (2), then wrap it around the neck, crossing over the safety pin. Tuck it neatly underneath to secure when you reach the end.

Open out the other end of the scarf so the fabric is wide, then cross this under the chin before wrapping the fabric over the head (3 & 4).

Pin the scarf ends at the back of your head to secure in place (5).

29

The BABY BOW COVER-UP

29: The
BABY BOW
COVER-UP

Add a statement bow to the top of a headwrap to introduce impact and drama to a classic look. This one is a little tricky to master but once you've got it, practice makes perfect!

We used a 90cm square scarf to create this look.

Fold a large, silk square scarf in half to create a triangle and then place the fold at the nape of the neck (1).

With the point of the triangle facing down over the forehead, bring the other two ends round over the ears and tie tightly at the top of the head (2), trapping the points of the scarf underneath.

Take the point of the triangle over to one side and tuck away neatly under the scarf near the ear (3).

Tie a bow at the front of your head with the two ends of the scarf (4). Tuck the ends of the bow into the headscarf and straighten the bow. Use pins to secure in place, if needed.

1

2

3

4

30

The KNOTTED 'FRONT, BACK AND SIDES'

30: The
KNOTTED 'FRONT, BACK AND SIDES'

A chic style for the colder months (that's great for keeping your ears warm!), this slouchy, knotted style goes well with earrings and a cosy winter coat.

We used a 60 x 190cm scarf to create this look.

Fasten the hair into a loose top knot.

Take a long, rectangular scarf to the back of the head (1) and bring the two ends of the fabric to the front.

At the centre, cross and then twist them back on themselves (2).

Now twist each end into a rope (3), then fasten in a small knot at the back of the headband (4).

You might want to work with the hair left exposed at the top so it sits nicely within the scarf.